A Tuneful Introduction

to the Third Position for Violin

NEIL MACKAY

Stainer & Bell

NOTE

It was Neil Mackay's intention that violin students, whether studying individually or in class tuition, should improve their musicianship by the enjoyment of melody. In his ever-popular teaching methods, including *A Tuneful Introduction to the Second Position*, the *First Year Violin Tutor* and *Second Year Violin Tutor*, and the *Four Modern Dance Tunes*, also available from Stainer & Bell, he combined his unique gift for gracious melodies with sensitive editing that leads students to a natural awareness of TEMPI and EXPRESSION MARKS, and of the punctuation of PHRASING, shown by commas or rests.

A Tuneful Introduction to the Third Position does not deal with the changing of position of the Left Hand. The only movement is the initial one from First to Third Position. Once this has been achieved, the hand remains in place throughout each melody. Students should remember to keep the thumb opposite the forefinger when the hand is in Third Position.

Neil Mackay wrote his tunes to be played on one string at a time by means of TETRACHORDS. A tetrachord is a scale series of four notes whose pattern is as follows: 1st – 2nd (TONE); 2nd – 3rd (TONE); 3rd – 4th (SEMITONE). The tetrachords on adjacent strings form major scales, and you will find that the three main keys are G major (A and D strings), D major (E and A strings) and C major (D and G strings).

The section entitled 'The Four Strings' contains a variety of finger patterns in different keys. These melodies may be used as reading material, or may be studied under the supervision of a teacher.

Easy piano accompaniments to the 24 pieces in *A Tuneful Introduction to the Third Position* are also available, catalogue number H419. Their composer, Richard Allain, has retained the essential simplicity and beauty of the originals in a fresh and engaging way. His arrangements will be welcomed by all teachers and pupils wishing to extend their use of Mackay's melodies, either as attractive concert repertoire, or as material to enhance the range of music-making within the individual lesson or class.

Autumn 2009

A Tuneful Introduction to the Third Position

The A String

Play the A string tetrachord and pause on note D with the 3rd finger.
Move the hand up to 3rd position and play the same note with the 1st finger.

1 . . . . . means keep finger on the string.

⌣ or ⌣ means a SEMITONE between the notes.

Waltz

simile means continue in the same manner.
The 1st finger should remain on the A string throughout the *Waltz* and *Jasmine* (page 2).

The Bow

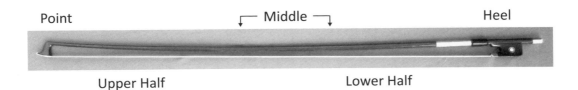

Jasmine

Practise in the Upper Half part of the bow, and stress the accented notes.
When the rhythm is altered by stressing notes which are
not normally accented, the effect is known as SYNCOPATION.

Puffing Billy

When you are sure of the intonation, practise the following bowings:
(a) STACCATO using the Upper Half bow
(b) SPICCATO using the Lower Half bow

The D String

The D string fingering is exactly the same as you have practised on the A string.

French Folk Song

This little tune can be played in three different parts of the bow:
(a) MIDDLE bow
(b) UPPER HALF bow
(c) LOWER HALF bow

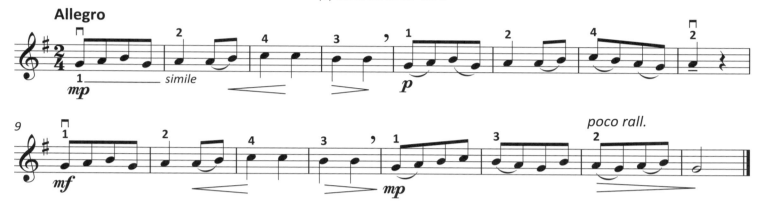

An Old Wife's Tale

The music should portray a real old gossip.
To obtain the desired effect, play mainly off the string between middle and heel of bow.
Bars 9 to 12 should be played in the Upper Half on the string.

The Minnow

Play between middle and point of bow. Stress the accented notes and take quick up-bows on the quavers.

Allegro moderato

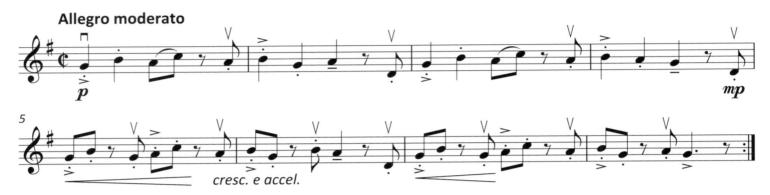

D and A Strings

Play the D string tetrachord followed by that of the A string and the result is the scale of G major.

Arpeggio

1= means 1st finger covering two strings at the same time.

Practise also using a bow to each bar.

Gavotte

The 1st finger can be kept down from beginning to end of the Gavotte.
Play the quavers SPICCATO (off string) near middle to lower half of bow.
Remember to stretch the 4th finger for C♯ in bar 6.

Grazioso

Irish Jig

Use the Upper Half of the bow throughout. Stop the bow momentarily between the two up bows.

The Huntsman

Play in the Upper Half bow. When this has been mastered, practise the two bowings given below.

etc.   Middle Bow (off the string)

etc.   Lower Half (lift bow quickly on UP-BOW quavers)

The E String

The E string fingering is the same as that used on the D and A strings.

Melody

Watch your left hand when playing on the E string. Keep the back of the hand in line with the forearm.
To check on your left hand position, practise in front of a mirror.
Bend your knuckles and play with the tips of the fingers.

Moderato

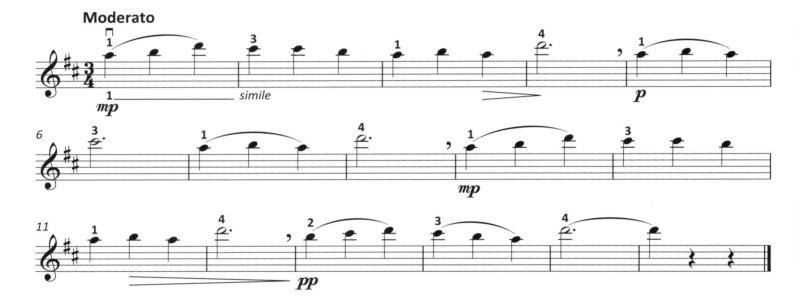

A and E Strings

Play the A string tetrachord followed by that of the E string and the result is the scale of D major.

Practise also with 2 and 4 notes per bow.

Arpeggio

Practise also using a bow to each bar.

German Folk Song

Start the up-bow in the Lower Half. In bars 4, 8 and 12, lift your bow off during the quaver rest so that the following quaver may start in the Lower Half bow. Stretch the 4th finger for G♯ in bar 11.

Swiss Air

The G String

Keep your left elbow tucked under the violin and let the thumb slide under the neck.
This will ensure a good left hand position and correct finger action.

The Grenadier

Bowings: (a) Upper Half STACCATO
          (b) Lower Half SPICCATO

G and D Strings

Play the G string tetrachord followed by that of the D string and the result is the scale of C major.

Practise also with 2 and 4 notes per bow.

Arpeggio

Practise also using a bow to each bar.

The Merry Whistler

Lullaby

Keep the 1st finger on the string until the next 1st finger position is indicated.
Make the bow changes as smooth as possible throughout.

The Four Strings

So far, the melodies have been on a single, or two adjacent strings.
The following tunes cover the four strings and each one is written in a different key.
In order that you may not be confused by the finger patterns, each melody is introduced by a series of tetrachords.
These tetrachords show the position of tones and semitones on each of the four strings.

C Major

Hungarian Dance

G Major (F♯)

Water Sprites

D Major (F♯ C♯)

Twilight Tango

A Major (F♯ C♯ G♯)

Hopscotch

E Major (F♯ C♯ G♯ D♯)

The Page Boy

F Major (B♭)

The Ridges

B♭ Major (B♭ E♭)

The Cobbler's Song

E♭ Major (B♭ E♭ A♭)

Rum and Butter

A♭ Major (B♭ E♭ A♭ D♭)

Ambleside

ALSO AVAILABLE FROM STAINER & BELL

24 Piano Accompaniments for Neil Mackay's
'A Tuneful Introduction to the Third Position'
by Richard Allain

Richard Allain's collection of piano accompaniments, of easy to intermediate difficulty, will add variety to individual or group tuition using Neil Mackay's 'A Tuneful Introduction to the Third Position' and provide attractive material for short yet effective recital items. The piano parts are fully compatible with this volume.

Catalogue No: H419
ISMN 979 0 2202 1964 1